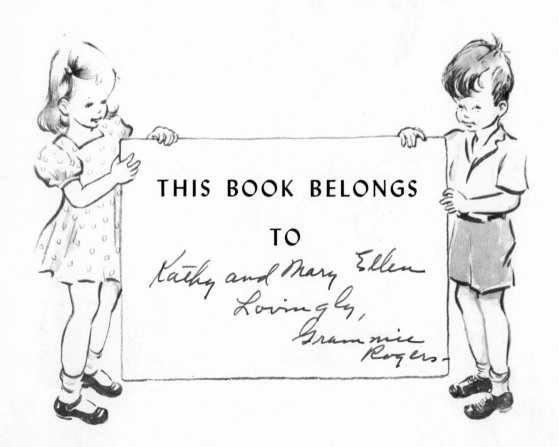

THIS BOOK BELONGS

TO

Kathy and Mary Ellen
Lovingly,
Grammie
Rogers.

TELL ME ABOUT GOD

BY MARY ALICE JONES

ILLUSTRATED BY PELAGIE DOANE

RAND McNALLY & COMPANY

NEW YORK   CHICAGO   SAN FRANCISCO

To Alice Rowe Who Asks Questions

CONTENTS

In quoting the Bible text, the King James Version is used, except in a few cases where, for the sake of simplicity and clarity for present-day children, a slight modification in the form is made. *Thee* and *thou* are retained in referring to God; otherwise, they are changed to *you*.

TELL ME ABOUT GOD

TELL ME ABOUT GOD

MOTHER, tell me about God," Bobby asked.

"What do you want to know about God, Bobby?"

"*All* about him."

His mother smiled. "Nobody knows all about God, Bobby."

"Not even you and Daddy?"

"Not even the wisest men in all the world."

"Why don't they?"

"Some things are so great and so good that we cannot understand them now. Nobody knows *all* about God, Bobby."

"Then tell me *some* about God," Bobby said.

And so his mother told him about God.

THE BIBLE HELPS US TO KNOW GOD

THE BIBLE helps us to know God, Bobby," his mother told him.

"How does it?" Bobby asked.

"It tells us God's plans for us. It tells us how other people learned to know God. It tells us how God helped people long ago. It tells us how God will help us now."

"Will you read me some about God?"

And so Bobby's mother opened the Bible and read to him. In this book are some of the verses she read.

God ... made heaven, and earth, and the sea, and all things that are therein.   ACTS 14:15

The Lord is good to all.   PSALMS 145:9

God is our ... help in trouble.   PSALMS 46:1

[13]

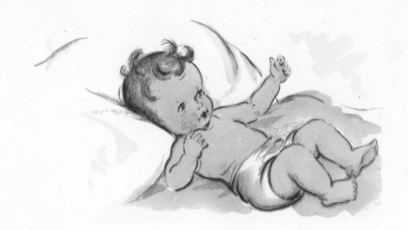

GOD LOVES US AND CARES FOR US

GOD loves you, Bobby," his mother told him.

"Does he love Mary, too?" Bobby wanted to know.

"Yes, dear, God loves the baby, too."

"The way you love us? And Daddy?"

"The way we love you, Bobby, and even more than that."

Bobby thought awhile. "Then he must love us a *lot*," he said.

"More than you can ever know. He loves you and cares for you."

"How does God take care of me?" Bobby asked. "I have you and Daddy."

"One of the ways God takes care of children is by planning families. In families there are mothers and daddies and children.

[14]

God depends upon the mothers and daddies to help him take care of the children."

"And does he depend on the children to help take care of the little babies?" Bobby asked.

"I am sure he does, dear. He depends on you to help take care of Mary."

Bobby hugged his mother. "I am glad God planned families."

His mother laughed. "So am I, Bobby."

He careth for you. I PETER 5:7

The Lord is thy keeper. PSALMS 121:5

God is love. I JOHN 4:8

GOD HELPS US TAKE CARE
OF OURSELVES

WILL GOD take care of me so I won't get hurt?" Bobby asked his mother. "And Mary, too?"

"God does not want any little children to get hurt, Bobby. He loves them. He plans for helpers to take care of them."

"Then why do children get hurt sometimes?" Bobby asked.

"I can tell you some of the reasons, dear. Sometimes the daddies and the mothers and the other big people do not help God take care of the children the way God planned."

"And sometimes the children do not do what their mothers

and daddies and the other big people tell them," Bobby said.

"And sometimes people do not think about other people and hurt them," his mother added.

"When they drive too fast?" Bobby asked.

"Yes, that is one way. And then sometimes the children do not use their eyes and their ears the way God planned for them to do," his mother went on.

Bobby thought a minute. "Like today when I almost ran into the street without looking," he remembered.

His mother nodded her head. "God planned for us to see and to hear so we can help him take care of ourselves."

The hearing ear, and the seeing eye, the Lord hath made even both of them. PROVERBS 20:12

The Lord hath been mindful of us. PSALMS 115:12

GOD IS ALWAYS NEAR

HOW do I know God is here?" Bobby asked. "Why can't I see him, Mother?"

"No one sees God with his eyes, Bobby," his mother told him. "We do not see him as we see each other. But we know he is here."

"How do we?"

"Close your eyes and think a moment."

Bobby closed his eyes and was very quiet.

His mother spoke softly. "All around us are light and air. In the sky the sun is shining. In the garden flowers are growing. In the house there are Bobby and baby Mary and Mother and Daddy who love each other. The light and the air, the growing flowers, the shining sun, and the love that people feel for each other make us know that God is here. Without God none of these things could be. Only God is great enough to plan these things."

Bobby opened his eyes. He looked all around him. He looked at his mother. "I want to know more about God," he said.

Be still, and know that I am God. PSALMS 46:10
He giveth to all life, and breath, and all things. ACTS 17:25

GOD PLANS FOR DAY AND LIGHT

I LIKE it when morning comes," Bobby said to his mother as he woke up on a sunshiny day.

"God planned for there to be daytime when it is light," she said.

"I can play out of doors in the daytime."

"You can run with Rover and not fall down, because it is light. And you can see the red roses and the yellow daisies."

"And I can find my wagon and my sandpile," Bobby said "I am glad God planned daytime when it is light."

> *And God said, Let there be light: and there was light.*
> *And God saw the light, that it was good.... And God*
> *called the light Day.* Genesis 1:3, 4, 5

[21]

GOD PLANS A BEAUTIFUL WORLD

BOBBY and Susan, who lived next door, were playing in the yard.
They were making up a song.

"I like the sunshine," Bobby sang, making up his own tune.

"I like the flowers," Susan sang, making up her tune.

Bobby's mother came out in the yard.

"Let's gather some flowers for the house," she said.

"Red flowers, and white flowers, and yellow flowers," Bobby
went on with the song, while they walked from bush to bush.

"Pink flowers and blue flowers," Susan added to the song.

When their basket had enough flowers for the house, Bobby
and his mother and Susan sat down on the grass under a tree.

[23]

They touched the smooth petals of the flowers. They looked at the sunny blue sky. They watched the leaves wave in the breeze.

"God planned the world to be a beautiful place," Bobby's mother said.

"Did God think of *everything?*" Bobby asked.

"What is it you are wondering about, dear?"

"Flower petals and the leaves. Did he plan little things, too?"

"Some of the nicest things in all the world are little things, Bobby. Little sea shells that have tiny rooms, and little butterflies that have lovely wings, and little birds that make gay music."

"Does God think of them all?" Susan asked.

"God is very great, Susan. God can think of more things than we can. We do not know how he thinks of everything. Some of his most beautiful thoughts are thoughts of the little things."

Not one of them is forgotten before God. Luke 12:6

He hath made everything beautiful in his time. ECCLESIASTES 3:11

[25]

GOD PLANS FOOD FOR US

Give us day by day our daily bread.   LUKE 11:3

IT'S time to eat! It's time to eat!" Bobby sang, as he sniffed the pleasant smells coming from the kitchen.

"Oh, no, Bobby. It is only four o'clock," his mother told him.

"But I smell it."

"I am making some peach preserves — the kind Daddy likes so much. And they do smell nice."

"*Um-m-m*," Bobby sniffed. "Peach preserves! May I have some?"

[28]

"I think we may have some for supper. They seem to be almost ready. When Daddy comes we will have a surprise for him."

Bobby stood near the stove and watched the thick, bubbling preserves.

"I am glad you plan good food for us," he told his mother.

"I like to help plan your food, Bobby. But other people help, too, you know. And God plans it first of all."

"How does he? You do it right in this very kitchen."

"Not all by myself, dear. There would not be any food if it were not for God's plan."

"Show me," Bobby asked.

His mother looked at the peach preserves. They needed a little while longer to cook. She could leave them.

She went over to the table and showed Bobby a carrot.

"It is muddy," Bobby said.

"It grew in the ground. Once it was a little seed. Somebody planted it and covered it with earth. The sunshine warmed it. The rain watered it. And it grew and grew until it was a carrot with a green, feathery top."

"Then what happened?"

"When it was ready to be food, someone pulled it out of the ground and someone brought it to our house. And I will clean it and cook it for your supper. But it was God who planned for it to grow. Without God there would not be any carrots."

"I like carrots," Bobby said. Then he remembered the pleasant smell. "And I like peach preserves, too. Did God plan them?"

His mother laughed. "I am not sure about the preserves, dear. I think God planned the fruit trees and left it to us to plan how we would use the fruit."

Give thanks unto the Lord . . . who giveth food to all. PSALMS 136:1, 25

[30]

GOD GIVES US WATER

I AM thirsty," Bobby told his mother when he came in from play. So he had a glass of cool water.

"I like water when I am thirsty," he said.

"So do all people, Bobby. That is why God plans for us to have water to drink."

"And for Rover? And for all the dogs, too?"

His mother nodded her head.

"And the birds and the rabbits and the cows, too?" Bobby went on.

"Yes," his mother answered, "God plans water for all creatures. And for the flowers and trees, too. God knows that every living thing needs water."

"That is why it rains," Bobby said. "I don't like it to rain. I like to play in my yard." He thought awhile. "But I think the trees like the rain."

"I think they do, too."

Just then Bobby saw that the sun was not shining. He looked out. There were dark clouds in the sky.

Bobby ran out of doors, and then he ran back in again.

"It's going to rain! It's going to rain right now!" he called to his mother.

"Let's put the windows down quickly," his mother said.

So Bobby and his mother hurried from room to room and put down the windows. And just as they had closed the last window, splashes of rain fell against the glass.

"Here it comes! It is going to be a big rain. The trees will have a big drink of water today."

Everyone that thirsteth, come . . . to the waters. Isaiah 55:1

God sendeth the springs into the valleys. . . . They give drink to every beast of the field. Psalms 104:10, 11

Bobby watched the rain making little rivers down the window glass. "Where does the rain go?" he wanted to know. "The part the trees don't need."

"I can't tell you where all of it goes, Bobby. But some of it goes to rivers. Men put some pipes in the rivers and the water runs through the pipes to our house."

Bobby turned on the water in the bathtub. "And I can have a bath," he said. "I think we need lots of water. It's a good thing God thought of water for us, isn't it, Mother?"

> *God giveth rain upon the earth,*
> *And sendeth waters upon the fields.* JOB 5:10

GOD HELPS US IN TROUBLE

Fear not . . . I will help you. Isaiah 41:10

THE wind was blowing hard. The lightning was making big flashes in the sky. The thunder was rolling with a loud noise. Bobby sat near his mother on the couch.

"It is making too much noise," he said.

"It is making a big noise, Bobby. Suppose we watch the lightning. We call the noise thunder, but really it is the lightning that causes the noise."

"I don't see why God makes it so noisy. It makes people afraid. It might hurt people, too."

[37]

"I think there is a reason for lightning, Bobby."

"But why does God let it hurt people sometimes?"

"We do not know all about our world, dear. Not even the wisest men. We do not know all about lightning yet. But God knows. Some day we may know."

"Will God keep it from hurting us?"

"Look, Bobby. Look at the fire in the fireplace. How good it feels on this stormy night! But what would happen if you put your hand in the fire?"

"It would hurt. But I wouldn't do that. I know better."

"Of course you do! You know about fire. But what about the baby? Mary doesn't know about fire yet. If she should put her hand in the fire she would get burned."

"Yes, she would. So we watch her."

"That is the way it has to be, Bobby."

Bobby thought it over.

"The fire *has* to be hot to keep us warm," he said.

"Fire is *good* because it keeps people warm. God planned it because we need it. But it *hurts* when anyone puts his hand in it."

"We have to learn about it," Bobby decided.

"That is the way it is. We have to learn about things in our world. Sometimes they hurt us because we do not know about them," his mother said.

"Like lightning?" Bobby asked.

"Maybe lightning is like that. We haven't learned all about it yet. But we are learning more about it all the time. And some day we may know as much about it as we know about fire now."

Bobby thought awhile. "Does God know all about it now?" he asked.

"Yes, dear, God knows all about it now."

I am with you, and will keep you.   GENESIS 28:15

What time I am afraid,
I will put my trust in thee.   PSALMS 56:3

GOD WANTS US TO HELP

BOBBY was feeling cross. "I wanted that radish to grow," he said. "Why didn't God make it grow, Mother?"

"I can think of one reason, Bobby. You forgot to water it."

"God could make it grow anyway. He can do anything."

"Anything that it is *right* for him to do, dear. But God has planned it so that there are some things he leaves for us to do," Bobby's mother explained.

"But sometimes we forget."

"Yes, sometimes we forget. And sometimes we do not take time to learn to do what God depends on us to do."

"Does God get angry with us when we forget?" Bobby wanted to know.

"I do not think God is angry with us, Bobby. He loves us, you see, even when we do not do the things we should. But I think he is sorry."

"And he doesn't do it for us? Like watering the garden, I mean."

"Do you think it would be a good plan if he did? If he treated you as if you were baby Mary who has to have everything done for her?"

"I would not like to be treated like the baby," Bobby decided. "I should have remembered to water my garden."

We are workers together with God.   I Corinthians 3:9

My Father worketh . . . and I work.   John 5:17

GOD IS VERY GREAT

BOBBY was looking at the stars. There were big bright stars, and there were tiny little stars, and they made pictures in the sky.

"How many stars are there, Mother?" he asked.

"There are many, many more than anyone can count, Bobby."

"I want to know all about the stars," he said.

"Some day you may know much more than you know now, dear. But only God knows *all* about the stars."

"Why can't I know all about them, too?" Bobby asked.

"Only God is great enough to know *all* about his world. There are many things that we can only wonder about."

God doeth great things past finding out . . . and wonders without number. JOB 9:10

The heavens declare the glory of God. PSALMS 19:1

GOD MADE THE NIGHT

*And God made two great lights; the greater light to rule
the day, and the lesser light to rule the night.* Genesis 1:16

BOBBY had on his sleepers and was all ready for bed. He looked
out of the window. He saw the moon. It made a soft light. His
mother looked out, too, over Bobby's shoulder.

"God planned the nighttime, and the moon, Bobby."

"Did he plan the moon to shine in the dark?" Bobby asked.

"I think he did."

Bobby and his mother watched the moon. It seemed to sail
among the clouds.

"The moon is not like the sun," Bobby said.

"You would not like it to be, would you, dear? If the moon
were bright, like the sun, you might not go to sleep."

[48]

"I like it the way it is."

"God plans sleep for us, too, Bobby," his mother told him.

Bobby yawned. "It is nice to go to sleep when I am sleepy."

"And to rest and feel ready for play when you wake up."

"Does God think of everything?" Bobby asked.

"You can count on it, Bobby. God thinks of everything we need to make us happy."

"Good-night, God," Bobby said. "I'll go to sleep now."

He giveth his beloved sleep.   Psalms 127:2

GOD WANTS US TO TALK WITH HIM

IS GOD too busy for me to talk to him?"

"No, Bobby, I think God is never too busy for you to talk with him," his mother said.

"I think he would get tired. He has so much to do."

"God does not get tired, Bobby. He isn't like us. He doesn't have to rest. He is God. You can always depend upon him."

"Does God want me to talk with him about everything?"

"I think God wants you to talk with him about anything that you wish to talk to him about, dear."

"Then may I ask him for a rabbit?"

"Are you sure you want to ask him for a rabbit, Bobby? Are you sure that is a good way to talk with God?"

"But I *want* one."

"Many, many people want many, many things. But some of the people have decided to trust God about them."

"But how will he know I want a rabbit if I don't tell him?"

"Because God knows *you*, dear. He knows what you want. And he knows more than that. He knows what will really be good for you. He knows better than Mother and Daddy know."

Bobby thought it over. "Daddy said it would be better to wait until I was bigger," he remembered.

"Yes, he thought it would be better to wait until you could take care of the rabbit by yourself. He thought Mother would not have much time to help you, because she has the baby."

Bobby thought some more. "Maybe I will just talk it over about the rabbit," he decided. "I will say, 'When I can take care of it I would like to have a rabbit.' "

"God will hear you, dear, whatever you talk about with him. But often there may be reasons that you do not know why it is not good for you to have many things that you think you want. Can you remember that God always hears you and loves you?"

"Even if I don't get what I want?" Bobby asked.

"You can count on God's love, dear, whatever happens."

Your Father knoweth what things you have need of, before you ask him. MATTHEW 6:8

Who trusteth in the Lord, happy is he. PROVERBS 16:20

Thou wilt hear me, O God. PSALMS 17:6

He that keepeth thee will not slumber. PSALMS 121:3b

God loved us, and sent his Son. I JOHN 4:10

GOD SENT HIS SON

BOBBY showed his mother a picture of Jesus. His teacher at church had given it to him.

"Tell me about Jesus," he asked.

"God loves us so much, Bobby, that he sent his son, Jesus, to tell us about it."

"How did Jesus tell us?"

"He did more than just tell us. He showed us. He helped those who were sick. He played with the little children and told them stories. He was kind to those who were sad. He said, 'See, I love you. That is why I want to help you. God loves you, too. And God wants to help you, too.' "

"Did the people listen to him?"

"Many of them did. And they understood about God's love. Jesus showed them what it meant. They said, 'God is like Jesus. He loves us.' "

"Were the people glad?"

"Those who listened to Jesus were very glad, Bobby. They felt happy. They said, 'We feel all made over. We are not sad or afraid any more. We know God loves us, whatever happens to us.' "

"What else did Jesus tell the people?" Bobby asked.

"He told them God's plan for them. He told them how God wanted them to live together. He said, 'Love one another. Help one another. Share with one another.' "

"What did the people do?"

"Some of them said, 'Jesus is telling us God's plan for us. It is a good plan. It will make people happy. We will live the way he says.' "

"What did the other people do?"

"The other people did not listen to Jesus. They did not want to know God's plan for them. They wanted to have their own way. And they made many people unhappy."

"If I had been there I would have listened," Bobby said.

"Would you, Bobby? I am glad. What Jesus said is still God's plan for us. We can listen to him now."

GOD WANTS US TO HELP
EACH OTHER

WHY should I let Susan play with my wagon?" Bobby asked his mother. "I want to play with it myself."

His mother smiled. "Let me ask you a question first, Bobby. Why should Daddy fix your wagon when he wants to read the paper?"

Bobby looked surprised. "Why, I asked him to."

"You were glad he fixed your wagon, weren't you? You liked it because he did?"

"Yes, I liked it. I needed my wagon."

"You see how it is, Bobby. Daddy stopped doing something *he* wanted to do so he could do something *you* wanted him to do. And you like it."

Bobby looked at his mother a moment.

"Is that why it is good to let Susan play with my wagon? Because she likes it?"

"I think so, dear. I think that is part of God's plan for us. He wants people who live together to do things for each other. He wants us to make each other happy."

"Even if we don't *want* to?" Bobby wanted to know.

His mother laughed. "Well, Bobby, if you try it awhile maybe you will find out that you do want to. Mother and Daddy want to do what you like. That is what loving people means."

Let us love one another: for love is of God.   I John 4:7

GOD HELPS US TO BE GOOD

WHY did God let me hit John?" Bobby asked his mother. "It was bad. Yes, it was."

His mother smiled at him.

"Why, Bobby," she said, "God doesn't *make* you be good."

"Why doesn't he?"

"Because that isn't what God is like. He lets you decide. God helps you to know what is a good way to act and what is a bad way to act. God helps you to do what is good."

"How does he help me?"

"One way is by helping you to remember that hitting people hurts them," Bobby's mother told him.

"I did remember," Bobby said. "Before I hit John I remembered. I *wanted* to hurt him."

"Then, you see, you would not let God help you. You would not listen. You decided to do *your* way."

Bobby thought awhile. "It would be better if I had listened. My way was not a good way."

All that the Lord speaketh, that I must do.   NUMBERS 23:26
I am with thee, saith the Lord.   JEREMIAH 30:11
The Lord is near unto all them that call upon him.   PSALMS 145:18

GOD FORGIVES US

DOES God love me always?" Bobby asked his mother.

"You can be sure of it, Bobby. God loves you always."

"When I am good?"

"Yes, when you are good, God loves you."

"And when I am naughty?"

"When you are naughty, God loves you, too."

Bobby thought awhile. "Why does God love me when I am naughty?"

"God does not love the naughty ways, but he loves *you*."

"Then maybe I'd better not be naughty any more. But sometimes I forget."

"Most of us forget sometimes, Bobby. Even big people like Mother and Daddy. And sometimes we just *want* to do what is bad."

"Then what do you do?" Bobby wanted to know.

"Then we tell God we are sorry, and God forgives us and helps us to want to do what is good, and to remember."

"If I tell him I am sorry will he forgive me and help me to remember?"

"You may count on it, dear. You see, God *loves* you."

Thou, Lord, art good, and ready to forgive.   PSALMS 86:5

GOD LOVES ALL HIS CHILDREN

DOES God love everybody?" Bobby asked.

"Yes, Bobby, everybody."

"Rich people and poor people and people who live far away and *everybody?*" Bobby wanted to know.

"I am sure he does, dear."

"Even bad people who hurt other people?" Bobby went on.

"I think God is sorry when anyone hurts anyone else, Bobby. But I think God goes on loving everybody and trying to help each one be good."

"I don't love bad people."

"Most of us do not love bad people," his mother agreed.

"I don't see why God loves bad people."

"You see, dear, God is much wiser than we are. He knows more about people than we do. He understands all that they do. He knows that bad people are not happy and he feels sorry for them. He wants them to be good."

"Does he punish them to make them good?"

"We do not know just how God works to help bad people be good. But we know he loves them and forgives them and wants always to help them."

There is . . . one God and Father of all.   EPHESIANS 4:4, 6

Thou art a God ready to pardon.   NEHEMIAH 9:17

He maketh his sun to rise on the evil and on the good, and sendeth rain on the just and on the unjust.   MATTHEW 5:45

LET US GIVE THANKS TO GOD

BOBBY and his daddy had been for a walk. Bobby ran into the house and hugged his mother.

"We saw some baby kittens and some baby birds, and some ducks . . . and *everything*," he said happily.

"I am glad you had a good time, Bobby," his mother told him.

"It was the nicest walk I ever did have."

"I can tell it was a nice walk, dear. You look so glad."

Bobby climbed up on the couch by his mother. "God planned a nice world, didn't he?"

"God planned a beautiful and a good world, Bobby."

"We ought to be good, too. Yes, we ought."

"I think so, too, Bobby. God depends on us to keep the world beautiful and good as he planned it to be. That is the very best way to thank him for all the things that make us happy."

The earth is full of the goodness of the Lord.   PSALMS 33:5

Oh give thanks unto the Lord; for he is good.   PSALMS 118:1